The IEA Health a

Choice in Welfare No. 7

Is British Food Bad For You?

Is British Food Bad For You?

Vincent Marks

London
The IEA Health and Welfare Unit
1991

First published in 1991
by
The IEA Health and Welfare Unit
2 Lord North St
London SW1P 3LB

ISBN 0-255 36267-6

Typeset by the IEA Health and Welfare Unit
Printed in Great Britain by
Goron Pro-Print Co. Ltd
Churchill Industrial Estate, Lancing, West Sussex

Contents

Foreword

The food scares of recent years—salmonella, mad-cow disease, and listeria, to mention only the most prominent—have given the impression that some of the most commonly eaten foods, including eggs, beef and cheese, are not safe. In *Is British Food Bad For You?*, Professor Vincent Marks, a distinguished clinical biochemist from the University of Surrey, offers an alternative, and occasionally hard-hitting view of the risks involved in human food consumption. He acknowledges that there are some risks and urges, for instance, the introduction of better farming techniques to reduce the incidence of salmonella in hens, and advises against eating the brains or spinal cords of cattle in order to avoid the very small risk from BSE or 'mad cow disease'. But his central thesis is that the risks we face when eating have been much exaggerated by an emerging band of food safety lobbyists and food writers whom he dubs 'apocalyptics'.

It has proved possible to alarm members of the public because the uses and limitations of the scientific method are not sufficiently well understood. Science cannot produce certainty. No scientific proposition is absolute and always remains open to possible refutation by future experience or experimentation. But this reality does not render scientific conclusions indistinguishable from mere opinion, rather they represent the best corroborated statements of fact that can be made on present evidence.

Just as there can be no absolute certainty about the facts of science, so there can also be no absolute safety in food consumption. Professor Marks convincingly argues that much of the reasoning that underpins many recent food scares rests upon the expectation of an unattainable level of certainty. It is not uncommon to witness hapless government ministers being pressed by TV interviewers to give the public a cast-iron guarantee that controls have been introduced to ensure that no one will ever again be at risk from this or that food. If the food in question is beef, possibly infected with BSE, or uncooked eggs, possibly infected with salmonella, most of us might initially sympathise with the interviewer's demand. But the truth is that no such guarantee can realistically be given.

Professor Marks supports his argument by surveying the chief food controversies of recent times, including the hazards involved in taking vitamins and minerals as food supplements, drinking milk from cows treated with growth hormone, consuming caffeine, sugar and irradiated foods, and the risks of contracting listeriosis from cheese, salmonella from eggs and bovine spongiform encephalopathy from beef.

In a highly politicised world we have become used to expecting a string of public policy recommendations to resolve issues, but according to Professor Marks, the remedy lies not primarily in government regulations but in raising public understanding of the value and limits of scientific knowledge. Without this improvement we will remain easy prey for the purveyors of the next food scare.

The Institute of Economic Affairs does not express a corporate view in its publications, but we have published this paper as a timely contribution which brings much needed balance to the emerging debate about the safety of our food.

David G. Green

The Author

Professor Vincent Marks, MA, DM (Oxon), FRCP (London and Edinburgh), FRCPath, is Professor of Clinical Biochemistry at the University of Surrey, Guildford and Head of the Department of Clinical Biochemistry and Nutrition at the Royal Surrey County Hospital, Guildford. He is currently President of the Association of Clinical Biochemists and a Vice-President of the Royal College of Pathologists. His department produces some 30 per cent of all postgraduates making a career in Clinical Biochemistry in the UK and his textbooks on the subject have been published in the USA, as well as in Britain, and translated into Italian. His research on human nutrition and metabolism has been concerned mainly with carbohydrates and fats of the diet and has led to invitations to speak on the topic at numerous international meetings.

1

Introduction

It is impossible to pick up a newspaper, women's magazine or colour supplement, or to switch on the television and radio these days without being subjected to some new horror story about the hidden threat to our health. Was it ever thus, or is it some new phenomenon. Edith Efron[1] has described people who exaggerate the dangers of modern living as 'apocalyptics'. Others have called them 'food terrorists' or 'food Leninists'—reflecting the author's own perception of the motives of such individuals.[2] Why at a time when the general health of the population has never been better—to judge from the few objective criteria available to us, such as infant mortality and life expectancy—are so many people preoccupied with early death?[3] Why, when the quality of food available to the general public has never been higher, are there so many food-linked scandals, both real and apparent?

It is clearly impossible in a brief essay of this nature to do more than suggest an answer to these questions, and allude to some reasonably well-documented examples of the genre by way of illustration. Most contain, as do many myths, a tiny germ of truth, which (through a series of illogical arguments and extrapolations or plain ignorance of the facts) has been converted from an interesting observation, worthy of further investigation, into an earth-shattering discovery of hidden dangers or even sinister plots by food growers, manufacturers and distributors—usually in cahoots with Government—to poison the populace.

A major contributory factor to this explosion of outrageous gobbledy-gook has been the growth in the number, and availability to the media, of instant experts whose knowledge of the subject under discussion is at best of a meagre and superficial kind, but who, because of their access to the mass circulation modes of communication, or their willingness to perform on or in it, influence public opinion far beyond their worth.

Expectations Of Health

Food and drink are at the very top of the hierarchy of human needs—well ahead of shelter, clothing, comfort and leisure. None of these is valued above good health; at least, not by those who can afford a choice. We do not know precisely when the expectations of good health became a feature of normal human life, nor do we have a very precise definition of what good health really is. The dictionary definition of health as 'soundness of body; that condition in which its functions are duly and efficiently discharged' is no longer adequate as it omits the qualifications of continuity and duration of life. Many people going about their lives in the community, and considered by themselves (and others) to be perfectly healthy, can be shown by modern methods of investigation to be at increased risk of suffering serious injury or death from any number of causes. Expectations of longevity and its realisation are therefore 'qualifiers' of health, and this can only be assessed after the event (i.e. the death of the subject!). Nevertheless, gradual recognition of the importance to our well-being of environmental factors (about which we can do something) as well as of various inherited traits about which we can at present do nothing, has had a profound effect upon our perception of health and healthy living. Food and drink are for most of us who do not work in hazardous occupations, the most important factor in the environment with regard to health. It is not altogether surprising, therefore, that real or perceived reductions in their quality have attracted the attention of the apocalyptics who seem to be completely unaware of the very real improvements that have taken place in both over the past half-century compared with the millennia that preceded it.

In earlier times, it was accepted that life was hazardous and that illness was just around the corner—especially if you were poor. It was taken for granted, even by the rich, that a fair percentage of their children would die, if not at birth, then shortly afterwards, and that childbirth itself was an extremely risky business. It was only with the eradication, in the early part of the present century, of the major killing diseases resulting from infections caused by a combination of poor hygiene and malnutrition, that the odds against dying young became sufficiently good to make worrying about the quality of health in adult life a worthwhile activity.

It is almost invariably forgotten (or more likely, deliberately suppressed) by those who attribute a purported but unsubstantiated deterioration in food quality to scientific and industrial intervention, that it was just such intervention that produced the revolution in food production, preparation and preservation earlier in this century, from which we are still continuing to benefit and which enables the world to support a population many times larger than was ever possible before. Without access to modern agricultural methods and the industrial packaging, processing and handling of food—which we now accept as commonplace—the likelihood of the countries in the EEC being self-sufficient in food for its 250 million or so inhabitants, would be extremely low, and the ability to feed the populace of large cities such as London and Paris, would be non-existent.

2

Anti-Science

'Society no longer trusts Science'[4]

In order to understand the philosophy of the apocalyptics it is necessary to say something about the growth and nature of the anti-science movement upon which it depends. Natural philosophy or science as we know it today, with its insistence upon the demonstrable reproducibility of evidence and the value of experimentation, though comparatively new is nothing more than a method of unravelling the secrets of nature. It has replaced, though not completely, the authoritarian and superstition-based concepts of nature that have dominated human thought and behaviour since the beginning of time, and still find favour among large sections of the world's population. The enormous benefits that have accrued to mankind as a result of the growth of science—and its related and dependent disciplines of chemical, electrical, civil and mechanical engineering—during the 19th and 20th centuries led to admiration for scientists and what they were doing to improve man's quantity and quality of life. This admiration continued until shortly after the Second World War, when the opprobrium attached to nuclear weapons fell not upon the politicians who possibly deserved it, but upon scientists, who did not.

The backlash against science and the espousal of authoritarian fundamentalism is unfortunately not confined to the Middle East. In other parts of the world it has, paradoxically, been adopted by those who have benefited most from the improvements in quality of life made possible by developments in science, especially physics and biology. It is these people—who are both ignorant of the great help that science has been to them and frightened by what they neither know nor understand—who comprise the population from whom the apocalyptics draw their support and strength. These, mainly middle-class, scientifically ill-informed individuals feel more comfortable with things that are naively or exploitatively referred to as 'natural'—without understanding quite what that term means—than they are with products they perceive as being manufactured or synthetic.

This is not a new phenomenon. People have always subscribed to the idea that panaceas exist, if only they (or at least someone who knows how to use them) could be found.

In its most extreme form the quest for panaceas and Nirvana leads to cultism, but less severe forms are very common. Included in this category are people who believe that there are 'good foods' or 'healthy foods' with special intrinsic virtues which are known about by only a few special people whose knowledge transcends science, but which they are prepared to share with true believers, usually for the price of a book, or sometimes more. People of this ilk—whom I call the *literate ignorami*—also believe in the unattainable concept of Absolute Safety, never having heard of Paracelsus' famous dictum[5] that there is no substance that is not toxic provided the dose is right. They are especially susceptible to the charms and wiles of charlatans and hucksters, who have always been with us, as they are today often in the guise of sincere and truly concerned people who want to share their prejudices with us (for a price!).

In its most blatant form, exploitation of the gullible is through the sale of worthless, if not actively harmful, nostrums, elixirs or medicines. These are often marketed as 'Health Foods' or 'Nutritional Supplements' in order to circumvent laws designed to protect the public from the sale of potentially harmful drugs and medicines. Many 'nutritional supplements' are sold at greatly inflated prices, compared with identical or frequently much purer products which are available from reputable chemical suppliers but which do not carry spurious or misleading labels. Two recent examples of worthless 'food supplements' causing damage are 'organic germanium'—which was heavily promoted as an essential nutrient when it is not—and tryptophan, which *is* an essential nutrient in the diet when taken as protein, but not when taken as a contaminated panacea or drug masquerading as a food.[6]

What is Science—What is a Scientist?

A more subtle, but even more pernicious form of huckstering than the actual sale of worthless panaceas, is to publicise them or write books, magazine articles, radio or television programmes extolling their virtues. Alternatively, authors may purport to expose the dangers of eating this or that food or diet, with no more evidence for their views than assertion!

It has always been the practice of hucksters not only to trade upon the fears they create in their audience, but to divert attention away from themselves by besmirching the good name of their critics. So it is today. Some of the most notorious of today's hucksters have the effrontery to accuse scientists whose work is of the highest ethical and internationally recognised standards, but of whom they disapprove, as being in the pocket of those who fund their research. The intention is to make such workers appear unreliable and untrustworthy witnesses. This attempt by the apocalyptics and unscrupulous to divert attention away from the real issues is similar to that used by the pickpocket to distract the attention of his victim whilst relieving him of his wallet. In the game of character assassination it is generally not the quality of the scientist's work that the hucksters attack—since this is often beyond reproach—but the investigator's personal integrity. This sort of behaviour, which has no bearing on the subject matter under discussion, is anathema to scientists and similarly reputable people. It is, however, commonplace among gutter journalists and others who work on the basis that if you throw enough mud, some of it will stick.

I, for example, was reviled in the press when I first described, under the title of 'Muesli Belt Malnutrition', a condition resulting from the imposition upon young children by their overly anxious, usually middle-class, literate, but misguided mothers, of feeding régimes that were totally unsuitable for them. I was accused of being in the pay (pocket) of the sugar industry, the confectionery industry or even the food industry as a whole, as though the only possible reason for exposing problems caused by ignorance is financial.

In such an unpleasant and hostile situation, how can the ordinary person know whom to believe? Where, after all, do people get their information about most things that matter to them, especially in the field of health and safety? There is no simple answer, but as in most other fields of human knowledge, the reputation of the informant is important. In the world of science, an investigator's reputation is based largely upon the quantity and quality of his published work, as judged by his peers, both nationally and internationally, many of whom would be admirers as well as rivals for fame and fortune. Other people acquire justifiable reputations in different fields; on the stage, in films, the media or in sport, for example, and become famous. Their knowledge of things outside their own sphere of expertise may, however, be only average or less than average, tinged with the prejudices of the relatively uninformed. Yet, because such individuals are household names, their views are often given credence beyond their worth. This has always been so and is the basis of endorsement of products by famous people which is as common today as it was a hundred years ago—and just as unreliable!

A scientist's work is reviewed critically by his peers, that is, by people who actually understand what he says, and if it cannot withstand their criticism and be reproduced by those who are competent to do so, it will be discarded along with his reputation. Fraud in science is far from unknown but is probably more easily detected than in most other forms of human endeavour.[7] Unfortunately most scientists are poor communicators to anyone except workers with similar interests to themselves. Consequently, even the most distinguished scientists tend to be unknown outside the comparatively small circle of friendly or hostile critics within which they normally move. Even when the discoveries for which scientists are responsible have passed into everyday use, they themselves often remain unknown. On the other hand, the publicists of those discoveries,—who may understand very little about them—often become household names. Nowhere is this truer than in the health sciences, including nutrition and toxicology, where 'popular books', newspaper articles and magazine articles for the lay public abound. Many of these are themselves based upon books written by authors with more imagination than knowledge, so giving rise to a huge publishing industry which feeds upon itself like Chinese whispers.

The more remote from the source of the knowledge, and the longer the chain between the final article and the original experiments and observations upon which they are said to be based, the more likely it is to be misleading.[8] The reason is not hard to find. Many 'popular' writers on health and nutrition are abysmally ignorant of scientific thought and method. They know nothing of statistics and probability theory. They confuse observations (i.e. facts) with explanations of those facts (i.e. theories) and mistake speculation by scientists—which is at the core of the scientific method—with their considered judgments, which are based upon (but distinct from) observable facts.

It has, for example, been suggested that 'chronic fatigue syndrome', a common condition in almost every one of the 'developed' countries of the world, has any number of causes, including hyperventilation, hypoglycaemia, chronic viral infections (ME), food allergies and so on—but none of these suggestions have withstood critical examination. This has not prevented each one of the possible explanations being adopted by a special interest group as 'the cause' of chronic fatigue syndrome. It is, in my opinion, probable that a very small proportion of sufferers from this common illness do indeed suffer from one or other of the postulated causes, but that the vast majority do not. They are nonetheless labelled as such, and mistreated accordingly by 'health' practitioners—both medically qualified and non-medically qualified who have eschewed the scientific method, and prefer to rely instead upon what they call 'alternative' medicine but which is in fact 'traditional' or more accurately 'folk' medicine.

The scientific method is based upon the creation of knowledge by investigating nature through observation and experimentation.

An experiment is the device that scientists use for testing a hypothesis which can either be disproved or supported; a favourable result of an experiment does not (indeed, cannot) prove a hypothesis correct, only that it remains a possible explanation of the observed facts. The possibility always remains that it will be shown to be wrong by further experiments, although the likelihood grows smaller the more times it is tested and found not to be incorrect.

The scientific method does not permit of certainty—that is the province of dogmatists; it does, however, permit of knowledge being built on the firm basis of reproducibility and of objective evidence, free from personal belief or prejudice. A mere collection of facts is not what science is about; it is the integration of those facts into a coherent story by a scientist that distinguishes the system of knowledge we generally regard as scientific from that based on unconfirmed belief systems or 'Faith'.

3

Safety and Danger

> I often say that when you can measure something you are talking about and express it in numbers you know something about it, but if you cannot express it in numbers your knowledge is of a meagre and unsatisfactory kind.
>
> Lord Kelvin

Safety and danger are often seen as diametric opposites: something is either safe or it is dangerous; it cannot be both. This is naive and untrue. Safety and danger are merely different ways of expressing the same phenomenon. Something is safe if it has an acceptably low probability of being harmful or producing damage, while something is dangerous if it has an unacceptably high probability of being harmful or producing damage. Assessment of risk is a highly technical matter and one of the principles upon which the insurance business is built. In other words, it can often be described in numerical terms and evaluated financially. To the non-scientist, however, the assessment of risk is generally subjective and irrational. Why else would so many people exceed the speed limit in towns and on motorways, go hang-gliding, riding, mountaineering or potholing for fun; smoke cigarettes or drink alcohol to excess, trust charlatans and quacks with their health, yet worry about cholesterol?

In relation to food, and increasingly other aspects of the environment, the concept of risk is usually expressed as things being safe, on the one hand, or poisonous or toxic on the other. Toxicity, like safety, cannot be assessed or described in absolute terms. Everything is toxic provided the dose is large enough. For most substances, toxicity can best be described as the dose at which an increasingly large number of people predictably experience unpleasant or undesirable side effects. There are, however, always a few idiosyncratic individuals for whom even a 'normally' non-toxic dose of a substance is poisonous. Take strawberries, for example, or any other common item of food. These can ordinarily be eaten in huge amounts by almost anyone, but in a tiny minority of subjects they cause an allergic reaction from which that person may die. This bizarre phenomenon is the result of an abnormal immune response to a normally non-immunogenic substance. It can occur with virtually any foodstuff containing proteins. Even though these foods are not intrinsically harmful, in susceptible subjects they may be deadly. A recently well-publicised example was the near-death of someone who ate a vegeburger containing, unbeknown to him, peanuts, to which he knew he was allergic and ordinarily avoided like the plague.[9]

In contrast to foods which are ordinarily looked upon as safe, there are a large number of substances that have been known since time immemorial to be poisonous or toxic; arsenic, cyanide and strychnine have become ingrained in people's minds as more or less synonymous with evil. Viewed objectively, however, they are far less damaging or toxic, on a weight-for-weight basis, than many of the more newly discovered essential constituents of the diet, such as Vitamin D and Selenium. As long ago as the 16th century Paracelsus, a German chemist and father of toxicology, pointed out that to talk about the toxicity of a substance without reference to the dose is meaningless. In similar vein, Lord Kelvin pointed out some centuries later that without measurement knowledge is generally of a meagre kind. We must not, however, fall into the trap of believing that just because we have a lot of numerical facts at our disposal we necessarily know a lot about the subject. The axiom that there are lies, damn' lies and statistics was never so true, nor so heavily exploited as today in relation to human nutrition.

Human Nutrition

The basic elements of human nutrition, as we understand them today, were laid down during the early part of this century by scientists, most of whom would now be called biochemists. The importance of fats and carbohydrates as fuels and of proteins as the building blocks of the body were known about long before the beginning of the present century. It was, however, only following the discovery of the role of certain substances that are present in small amounts in the food and which make no contribution either to the fabric of the body itself or to the supply of energy that nutrition was born as a science and separated from home economics.

The various 'trace dietary substances' which are collectively known as vitamins and essential minerals (or trace elements) depending upon their chemistry are necessary because of their involvement in the regulation of metabolism, the process whereby the body converts one product into another of greater value to itself. Without an adequate supply of these dietary constituents the body cannot use its food properly. Deficiencies lead to specific illnesses which can be cured, or even better, prevented, by ensuring that foods containing all of them are included in that person's diet.

Since the 30 or so trace substances of dietary origin that are now known to be essential for a full and healthy life are not evenly distributed in different foodstuffs, the only way to ensure that they are all taken in adequate amounts is to eat as varied a diet as possible. This is more easily said than accomplished, especially for the poor. Indeed, deficiency diseases are, and always have been, rare amongst the better-off sections of the population who can afford to have a rich and varied diet, but very common amongst the indigent. Nutrition has, therefore, always had implications for politicians as well as for scientists.

Salesmen too have found the science of nutrition an interesting one. Vitamins, once they had been identified, purified and manufactured, appeared to provide the perfect panacea. They could be talked about, written about, and—more important—sold, to a public which had become aware of the complexities of nutrition without understanding it. In this way the legitimate growth of nutritional knowledge and its dissemination was hijacked by people who, in former times, were known as 'quacks', hucksters or nostrum-mongers, and better known for selling panaceas to gullible people than for their dedication to the truth.[10]

Vitamins and Minerals

The opportunity to sell 'nutritional supplements' which could circumvent the increasingly stringent regulations covering the sale of drugs and medicines that many governments, especially the United States of America, had introduced, was too good a chance to miss. Paradoxically, it is the very people who can afford to buy these products who are least likely to have any need for them or any other dietary supplements.

As far as the vitamins and trace elements are concerned, there is no evidence that more is better. Indeed for many of them there is strong evidence to the contrary. It was already well-known before the Second World War that anyone eating a variety of foodstuffs in amounts sufficient to maintain their bodyweight within reasonable limits was unlikely to have a nutritionally related disease. If they did, it was good evidence of an underlying illness such as malabsorption requiring medical rather than dietary treatment. This knowledge about what constitutes a healthy diet has still not been improved upon.

The people who are most likely to benefit from widespread dissemination of this knowledge are the public and those reputable farmers, manufacturers, distributors and retailers who maintain high standards of food quality. There is no margin in it for the purveyors of worthless food supplements and exotic foods of dubious nutritional value, but for which high prices can be charged providing they are thought to have value over and above that possessed by 'traditional' foods.

How is the man in the street to know what is the truth when he seeks information about nutrition, and from whom is he to get it? How is he to know if he is getting sufficient of the essential trace elements that he knows he requires when he is bombarded with false claims and false information from so many quarters, especially those who stand to gain most from spreading misinformation?

Take the recommended daily allowance or RDA concept, for example. This is misused by all sorts of people, many of whom either do not know what it is or, if they do, hope that others will not. RDA figures have been produced for most nutrients, including the macronutrients—that is, fats, carbohydrates and proteins—and are the amount of that substance (nutrient) that can be expected to satisfy the requirements of 90 per cent of people in a particular community. The RDA is not the amount of a nutrient that every person should have each day. If everyone ate the RDA of all of the nutrients, about 50 per cent would be getting well in excess of their actual needs. This probably would not matter much for some, possibly all, of the trace nutrients, but it would matter enormously for the macronutrients, i.e. the substances such as fats and carbohydrate that supply energy, whereas, if everyone ate the RDA, some would become painfully thin and others excessively fat.

Put differently, RDAs are nothing more than guestimates to enable those such as government officers, food economists and mass caterers, whose job it is to look after the food supply of populations, to get their figures approximately right. For individuals, RDAs can serve only as guidelines to the approximate amount of a particular nutrient they should be getting in their diet. Because most of the vitamins and many of the trace elements have a large margin of safety between the dose at which they are maximally effective and the dose at which they become toxic, little harm is done by eating up to, or even exceeding, the RDA, which is always set generously while differing quite markedly between countries. In the case of certain vitamins, such as Vitamins A and D, and some trace elements, such as selenium and iron, a person who takes concentrated 'dietary supplement' such as those sold in some pharmacies, health food shops and elsewhere, may exceed the toxic threshold and make himself ill without too much difficulty. Several examples of such self-induced illness have been reported in the quality newspapers in recent times,[11] but they do not commend themselves to the mass media as material for a hype or exposé.

The De Minimus Principle

Modern analytical methods developed by chemists, biochemists and physicists over the past 30 years or so, make a nonsense of many previous conceptions, including some of the laws relating to food safety and toxicity. An idea frequently bandied about these days is that it should be illegal to drive with any alcohol in the blood. This would make criminals of us all, since it is possible to demonstrate, using modern sophisticated analytical methods, that small but clinically insignificant amounts of alcohol circulate in the blood of most of us. It probably gets there as a result of fermentation of carbohydrate in the lower bowel but no-one knows for certain. To be realistic, therefore, a lower limit must be defined below which any amount of substance found must be considered indistinguishable from zero.

This rule applies equally to the contamination of food, and to the laws that regulate it. For example, lead has been recognised as a poisonous substance since Roman times and laws making it an offence to sell food containing it have been in operation for many years. Until recently, the methods available for measuring lead were insufficiently sensitive to detect and measure the tiny amounts that are ordinarily present in *all* foodstuffs, and not only those dangerously contaminated with it, so that when lead was found it was there in substantial amounts. Advances in measurement technology have changed all that.

Animal products, particularly those obtained from animals fed lead-contaminated foodstuffs, contain lead in amounts that can easily be detected and measured by modern techniques. The total amount of lead absorbed by anyone eating even heavily lead-contaminated animal products would, however, be very small indeed. The total amount of lead in the body, which mostly comes from paint and other lead-containing substances in the home and work environment, would not ordinarily be increased by anything more than a very small percentage except possibly when the lead-contaminated food comprised the sole or major constituent of the diet.

Recently a food scare arose when a consignment of cattle feed was heavily contaminated by lead during its passage to this country. Although a cause for concern, it was not a real threat to health except possibly to babies who were living solely on a diet of milk from cows that had been fed the contaminated feed. This is not how the problem was presented to the public by the mass media which grossly exaggerated the dangers of lead poisoning to the populace as a whole. For although the amount of lead in the cow's feed was large enough to constitute a severe threat to the health of the cows and did produce comparatively high concentrations of lead in their milk, the total amount of lead that any adult could get from this source was infinitesimal.

This example is not cited to minimise the original offence of supplying grossly contaminated feed to cows, but to show how, without quantifying the danger, what is really a very special problem affecting a very highly selected group of the population, can be presented as a general one affecting everyone, thereby causing unfounded and unnecessary alarm.

Bovine Somatotrophin (BST)

Another example of alarmism is the question of the safety of milk from BST-treated cows. This is a continuing saga due mainly, if not entirely, to anti-scientific scaremongering. Unlike the 'lead in milk' stories, it does not even have the justification that BST is toxic in the amounts at which it occurs in milk to anyone as far as we know, though we cannot of course be certain.

BST (otherwise known as bovine growth hormone) is normally produced in the pituitary gland of cows and enables them to grow and secrete milk. An analogous, but not identical substance is produced in the pituitary gland of human beings. In the absence of human growth hormone a child does not grow properly, whilst its over-production causes a rare form of gigantism. The isolation of Growth Hormone from the pituitary gland of cows was achieved in the 1930's but contrary to expectations could not be used for treating human dwarfism, even when it was caused by growth hormone deficiency, because it was ineffective. This is quite unlike diabetes, which responds just as well to bovine as to human insulin. Treatment of dwarfism due to growth hormone deficiency had to wait upon the availability of the human hormone which, until recently, could only be obtained with extreme difficulty and in minute amounts from pituitary glands removed from dead human beings. Consequently only a favoured few of the children who were likely to benefit were able to receive growth hormone treatment (but see below).

This has all changed as a result of the same triumphant application of bioengineering that has given us human insulin—and obviated the need to extract insulin from the pancreas of pigs and cows for the treatment of diabetes—to human growth hormone which has become available for the treatment of human dwarfism. Using the same technology but with a different genetic template, it has also proved possible to bioengineer bovine growth hormone (BST). This hormone not only makes calves grow larger and more quickly, thereby turning animal feed into meat more economically, it also improves milk yield from cows when given to them by injection.

The uproar caused by this contribution to the continuing application of science to animal husbandry bears no relation to any dangers it may pose to human health, though it may bear some relation to ethics. It has been implied by the apocalyptics that BST in the milk of cows treated with it makes their milk unsafe for human use. Exactly how, and in what way, is not specifically stated. It is true that bioengineered BST (like the endogenous, naturally produced hormone) does appear in the milk of treated cows at concentrations possibly some four to ten times higher than in untreated cows. Even so its concentration is still measured in parts per thousand million.

Although it is impossible to be certain, since virtually nothing ever is, the chance that a substance like bovine growth hormone —which has to be given by injection in order to have any biological effect, even in cows,—would have a toxic or other effect in human beings when taken by mouth, is so small as to be insignificant. BST is a protein and consequently would be expected, like all the other proteins in milk and which are generally present in thousands or even millions of times greater concentrations, to be destroyed by the normal digestive processes. Even if some or all of the molecules of BST in the milk we drank were, in some mysterious way, to escape digestion and be absorbed directly into our bodies, it is extremely unlikely that they would have any toxic or any other effects to judge from the experience many years ago when BST was used experimentally, but ineffectively, to treat human dwarfism. Whether the potential damage to the cows receiving BST is justifiable is another matter altogether and is related to the ethics of animal husbandry, not to human health.

Caffeine

> 'Too much coffee can put you in a straight-jacket', says Consultant Psychiatrist.

This statement was how a news item was introduced on local radio in London on 13 June 1990. What is the truth behind this alarmist statement? When he was finally interviewed the medical consultant did indeed say that the drinking of four or more cups of coffee could make one 'anxious, rude or possibly aggressive'. He did not say that it could lead to some people being put into a strait-jacket. The whole story could be dismissed as no more than the difference between a headline—designed to attract public attention—and the true story that followed and which was quite unexceptionable. Nevertheless it is the headline that is remembered, not the detail.

It has been known for at least 150 years that all caffeinated beverages, especially coffee, can cause a variety of subjective symptoms and even objective changes in behaviour when they are taken in excess. There is, however, nothing especially distinctive about the signs and symptoms associated with overdosing with caffeine. These can result from a variety of clinical conditions such as thyrotoxicosis or pheochromocytoma for which there are very specific and curative treatments and anxiety neurosis for which there are not! When caused by caffeine the symptoms are associated with high plasma caffeine levels and are specifically relieved by abstention from caffeinated beverages. Since the confidence with which a diagnosis of caffeine intoxication is made and imparted to a patient is often very convincing, a placebo response is extremely difficult to rule out and many people who believe themselves to be sensitive to the pharmacological effects of caffeine turn out not to be so when tested double blind. This is a technique in which neither the recipient nor the donor of the treatment knows whether the reputedly active agent rather than a placebo was administered until the trial has been concluded and the code, held by a third party, is broken.

Using modern analytical methods for the measurement of caffeine in blood, it is possible to get a very good idea of whether caffeine intoxication is responsible for someone's symptoms or not, and can be obtained without enforcing abstinence from tea, coffee and other caffeinated drinks. Only a very few cases of genuine caffeine intoxication have come to light from amongst the many hundreds and possibly thousands of people that my colleagues and I have tested over the years, even when caffeine intoxication was strongly suspected clinically. For the vast majority of people, caffeinated beverages are perfectly safe.[12] Their exclusion from the diet would leave a gap in people's fluid intake that would need to be filled by some other, probably less acceptable, drink from a health point of view. It would also reduce the pleasure many people get from caffeinated beverages which accounts for their universal popularity.

As a result of our own work and that of others, we know that most of the concerns expressed in the innumerable magazine articles purporting to have discovered the dangers of caffeine are nonsense. Caffeine does not, for example, cause cancer, high blood pressure or fetal abnormalities, all of which have been laid at its door at some time or another and shown to be false. But when have dull old facts been allowed to stand in the way of exciting new myths—especially in the writing of popular articles on the dangers of food and drink?

Children are less well able to handle caffeine than adults and it may accumulate in their bodies even when taken in doses that are not excessive by adult standards. There is, therefore, a genuine cause for concern about unbridled consumption of caffeinated beverages, especially cola drinks, by children and adolescents but up to now this possibility remains no more than speculation as reliable data are just not available.

Sugar

If the seemingly unorchestrated campaign against caffeinated beverages is 'over the top', then that waged against sugar is downright mischievous. The war against sugar is not new but began more than a century ago when sugar was linked with the slave trade. In its modern form, however, the battlefield is health. Sugar is held by the saccharophobes—including some who ought to know better—to be responsible for so many illnesses that it provides unlimited fodder for an army of authors and journalists. No single foodstuff has ever been so thoroughly investigated for possible detrimental effects upon health with such consistent lack of positive evidence as sugar over the past 20 years.[13]

Except for a role in the causation of dental caries, sugar has consistently been exonerated from blame in the causation of major disease.[14] Not that sugar actually causes caries, but it does encourage them. The immediate cause of dental caries is an infection of the tooth by an organism that uses sugar as one of its main foods. The organism responsible does not, however, distinguish between refined sugar that comes from a manufacturer and sugar that occurs as a 'natural ingredient' in most fruits and many vegetables. Indeed, there is every reason to believe that sugar in fruits, especially dried fruits such as raisins and dates, is more cariogenic —because of the sticky form in which it is eaten—than much of the so-called 'added' sugar. Similarly, sugar in fruit juices—which are always promoted as 'unsweetened'—is just as plentiful and cariogenic as sugar in sweetened tea and coffee and soft drinks which are condemned by the saccharophobes as 'unhealthy'.

None of the claims that sugar is responsible for illnesses such as gall bladder disease, cancer, heart disease, diabetes or hypoglycaemia, have been substantiated despite extensive research by impeccable internationally recognised investigators. The exoneration of sugar on scientific grounds as a cause of ill-health has had no effect upon its detractors, who like others of similar ilk do not let facts interfere with their theories. They persist in disseminating untrue allegations about the supposed toxicity of sugar, accusing those who disagree with them (often on the basis of their own scientific work and that of others they know to be unimpeachable) as being something less than honourable and in the pay of the sugar or confectionery industries.

Nowhere is distortion of truth more apparent than in the claims by food terrorists that sugary foods are responsible for hyperactivity in infants and violent behaviour in older children and adolescents. So persuasive have they been in their campaign that some judiciaries (none, as far as I know, in this country) have imposed participation in sugar-free dietary regimens upon juvenile offenders not, it is claimed, as a punishment but as part of the rehabilitation process![15]

So well known is the myth that 'sugar is bad for you' that anyone like myself who disputes it on the basis of the mass of contrary evidence is condemned by the food terrorists as irresponsible, when exactly the reverse is the truth. Many people have been persuaded not only to deprive themselves—when it probably does not matter—but also children and sick people dependent upon them, of good wholesome foods containing sugar which they would enjoy and from which they would also benefit. We see this happening not only in the domestic situation but, even worse, in our public hospitals where misguided zealots insist upon feeding sick and elderly patients with bulky high-fibre foods that they cannot or will not eat, whilst depriving them of palatable energy-rich food that they will, and which would provide them with the means of overcoming their illness.

Irradiation of Food

Mankind has always had a need to preserve food in order to make it available where and when it is required. Drying, pickling, fermenting and more recently bottling were the main methods employed by individuals until more modern, industrial techniques such as canning, chilling and freezing became available. These newer methods of preserving food were the result of advances in the science and technology of food processing and drew opprobrium from the anti-science lobby of their day. The most modern of all food preservation methods—namely gamma irradiation—is currently the subject of an outrageous and totally unscientific attack by today's opportunists, including 'food-writers' and political lobbyists, who are exploiting people's fears about radioactivity for their own nefarious ends.

Probably more is known about the effects of irradiation on food and its components than of any other food process.[16] This knowledge has been accumulated over the 50 years or so since irradiation was first used to render things sterile without having to alter their physical or chemical nature. The benefits to mankind of the controlled use of irradiation have long been recognised in medicine but have been overshadowed in the public arena by the dangers of unbridled radioactivity such as occur after nuclear explosions. These dangers do undoubtedly exist but the link between regulated and non-regulated irradiation is no greater than that between the danger of drowning in water and the benefits of drinking it. It is only by extrapolating far beyond data, implying guilt by association rather than on evidence and by fostering people's confusion between irradiation of food and radioactivity in food—which was highlighted by the Chernobyl disaster—that the scare mongers have been able to delude the people and even the Government into believing that food irradiation is harmful and should be banned. Fortunately the Government has recently seen sense and intends to permit regulated irradiation of food. How long will it take the apocalyptics to behave likewise?

4

Infections from Animals and Vegetables

The examples of media hype that I have quoted so far are as nothing compared with those relating to Salmonella in eggs, Listeria in salads and cheeses and Bovine Spongiform Encephalopathy (BSE). Each of these 'food scandals' attracted newspaper, TV and radio headlines for weeks at a time, with varying degrees of justification, but with predictable effect upon the industry and upon the public perception of food safety.

Listeriosis

Listeriosis made the headlines as a food-borne disease all over Europe in the autumn of 1987. Like so many food 'hypes' it had surfaced a year or two earlier in the USA, mainly as a result of a small number of well-publicised epidemics. For a time it provided a bonanza for food writers, investigative journalists and, of course, the perennial band of professional apocalyptics, some of whom went on to become involved in bigger and better publicised 'food scandals'.

The agent that causes listeriosis is any one of a large number of strains of listeria monocytogenes, which is a very widespread bacterium found in many foods. A special feature of this comparatively non-pathogenic organism is its ability to grow at domestic refrigerator temperatures, that is, at 4-6°C. The illness to which it gives rise, namely listeriosis, has long been known to pathologists and other medical practitioners, as an uncommon and sporadic infectious disease confined almost exclusively to pregnant women and their fetuses, newborn babies, the elderly and people who, because of other diseases such as AIDS (Acquired Immuno Deficiency Syndrome) which interfere with the body's immune system, cannot defend themselves against even the most trivial infections.

Compulsory reporting of listeriosis was introduced for the first time anywhere in the world following an epidemic in California in 1985 and gave some indication of the prevalence of the disease in the community as a whole. In California, it emerged that listeriosis occurred with a frequency of twelve cases per million of the population per year. As in the epidemic which gave rise to the legislation, almost all of the cases that were reported had occurred in subjects who were known to be susceptible. No common food source was apparent among the sporadic cases reported from California, nor has any common cause been found in other non-epidemic situations. In one epidemic, soft cheese and other dairy products were implicated as the main source of the infectious agent. In another, raw vegetables were implicated, whilst in yet another, ice cream and salami appeared to have been the main villains. There is, therefore, no common pattern of infectivity, nor is there any reason to believe that listeriosis is any more common now than it was in the past. It is however, undoubtedly better recognised and consequently more often diagnosed.[17]

Salmonella in Eggs

Bacteria of the genus Salmonella are responsible for many diseases, the best known, until comparatively recently, being typhoid and paratyphoid fevers, both of which are killers and spread mainly by the drinking of contaminated waters. Other types of Salmonella cause generally milder illnesses which are often referred to collectively as 'food poisoning' but which can, in the most severely affected cases (especially amongst the young, the elderly and the infirm) cause death.

Food poisoning caused by Salmonella has long been known to be associated with mass catering, especially when this involves the use of poultry dishes. Chickens and ducks constitute a large reservoir for the micro-organisms which do not seem to do the birds themselves very much harm. Salmonella, like most bacteria, are very susceptible to heat. Consequently food containing Salmonella organisms is ordinarily rendered sterile, and so made safe for eating, by the heat that is necessary to effect cooking. Ideally of course, only birds that were free from Salmonella would be used for human consumption, and freedom from infection of all foods must be the objective of food hygienists. It is an unfortunate fact that this ideal has not been achieved in Britain—nor anywhere else in the world, for that matter—and may never be completely attainable. Nevertheless, considering the widespread distribution of various pathogenic strains of Salmonella, the comparative rarity of Salmonella food poisoning indicates just how effective cooking is in keeping it under control. Most outbreaks or epidemics of food poisoning caused by Salmonella can be traced back to poor hygiene in the preparation or storage of food, especially poultry.

Eggs have long been recognised as a potential source of salmonellosis, although it was thought that this was invariably due to micro-organisms on the surface of the shell getting into the egg or onto the hands of the cook during the course of food preparation. If, because of poor hygiene or because food containing contaminated eggs was not heated to a sufficiently high temperature to kill all of the organisms, it could, unless eaten immediately, lead to sufficiently large numbers of the bacteria getting into the body to constitute a threat to health.

The idea that eggs with unbroken shells might themselves not only contain Salmonella but do so in sufficiently large numbers to cause disease in anyone eating them, surfaced in the USA in the spring of 1988. It arrived in this country some six months later. It led to one of the most enduring and most expensive food scandals of all time, culminating in the resignation of Edwina Currie from a ministerial post within the Government. The grounds upon which the scandal was based, namely that eating eggs that had not been hardboiled constituted a real hazard to health, was grossly exaggerated. Indeed the evidence that food poisoning has ever been caused by eating soft-boiled eggs or even raw ones for that matter, is anecdotal at best and based upon laboratory observations that a small proportion of eggs produced by hens infected with Salmonella become infected before the shell is fully formed whilst still in the hen's body. Perhaps the reason that this happening does not cause more problems is that infected hens also produce antibodies which they secrete into the eggs and probably prevent the bacteria from multiplying.

One consequence of the discovery that raw eggs can contain live Salmonella was the focusing of attention upon the high prevalence of Salmonella in hens, not only those used for laying, but also for eating. This was, and is, something that requires attention since although the risk of Salmonella food poisoning will probably never be eliminated completely, it can certainly be reduced by good farming practice. This includes screening poultry flocks by modern analytical methods for carriers of the infection and eliminating them. This move is possible and long overdue.

Bovine Spongiform Encephalopathy (BSE)

One morning Britain woke up to learn that our cows were suffering from a new disease, BSE, and that the eating of beef had become a hazard to life. Would BSE have provoked the same reaction in either the public or politicians had it not been for the visual impact of the appearance, night after night on television, of the same unfortunate cow stumbling in a farmyard as a result of infection with the disease? Almost certainly not.

BSE does seem to be a 'new disease', just as HIV is now and Von Economo's sleeping sickness or encephalitis lethargica was in the 1920's. Encephalitis lethargica assumed epidemic proportions in the 1920's but had almost disappeared by the 1930's; disappearing just as mysteriously as it had arrived. It left tens of thousands of people dead and thousands more permanently crippled, yet who knows of it today?

BSE was first reported in Britain some four years before the story 'broke'. The number of cases known to The Ministry of Agriculture, Fisheries and Food (MAFF) grew exponentially but the disease only achieved public recognition early in 1990, when it burst upon the scene under the name of 'mad cow disease'. So far, the occurrence of BSE in other countries has not been reported, though we do not know whether this is because of its absence or—as seems much more likely—the failure to recognise and report it.

BSE, like human illnesses, is recognised by the symptoms to which it gives rise. Diagnosis, however, depends upon the presence of characteristic neuropathological features which can only be ascertained at post mortem. These changes are similar to those seen in a number of other diseases which occur in man and animals and have been known about for many years. Their exact cause is still poorly understood but Gajdusek was awarded the 1976 Nobel Prize for Physiology and Medicine for discovering that they are caused by transmissible agents which differ both in their nature and form from all the other types of transmissible agents, such as parasites, bacteria and viruses which cause disease.

For a short time following their discovery, the agents causing these rare neurological diseases were known as 'slow viruses', but nowadays they are usually referred to as 'prions' to denote their proteinaceous nature without prejudice as to what they will finally turn out to be.[18] What makes prions especially worrisome to public health authorities is their resistance to inactivation by the physical and chemical agents, such as heat, that destroy ordinary bacteria and viruses. There is an extremely long incubation period between infection and the manifestations of disease, hence the earlier name of 'slow viruses', and they do not evoke conventional inflammatory reactions in the tissues. Most worrying of all, they do not evoke the normal immunological reactions including the production of antibodies which ordinarily work to neutralise the effect of extraneous organisms and toxins on the body. At a more practical level, antibodies provide a means of identifying infection with the causative agent and it is mainly through their ability to evoke antibodies that infections with the HIV viruses can be recognised before causing full-blown AIDS.

Prions are implicated in two naturally occurring but rare diseases in man. One of them, Kuru, is confined to people living in Papua, New Guinea. The other, Creutzfelt-Jacob disease, named after its co-discoverers, occurs sporadically throughout the Western World. At the peak of its incidence, Kuru was said to have been the cause of death of no less than 90 per cent of the women of the Fore tribe of Papua, New Guinea, who, because of tribal customs, came into very close contact with the brains of dead relatives, mainly by eating them. Following discontinuance of cannibalism in Papua New Guinea, the incidence of Kuru has all but disappeared, but not so with Creutzfeld-Jacob disease.

The natural mode of transmission of Creutzfeld-Jacob disease, in which the brain, at post-mortem, shows the spongiform appearance (i.e. the presence of 'bubbles' and 'holes') that is characteristic of it and of BSE, is still unknown. The occurrence of a mini-epidemic of what is normally a very rare disease was associated with one particular batch of human growth hormone prepared from the pituitary glands of dead people (see p. 18). How this particular batch of natural growth hormone became contaminated and why seemingly no other batches of growth hormone of any of the other hormones prepared in the same way have done so over the 20 years or more since they were first used for the treatment of human disease, remains a mystery.

Scrapie, a disease of the brain of sheep and goats, resembles Kuru and Creutzfeld-Jacob disease in man. It has been recognised for decades as being transmissible to certain other animals under experimental conditions, but has not become endemic in other species. It is thought to have been the cause of BSE, though the evidence is far from conclusive. Can human beings also acquire some form of spongiform encephalitis from eating the flesh of infected cows, and if so, can the risks be put into perspective, given the relatively few facts that are known about this rare group of diseases?

First of all, no-one ever seems to have acquired scrapie, Creutzfeld-Jacob Disease or Kuru by working with, killing or eating sheep or goats. In some societies, it is the custom to eat the brains of these animals as a delicacy. Nor does anyone appear to have acquired a spongiform encephalopathic disease through the use of insulin and other products of animal origin that are given by injection, even though many of them are derived from offal.

The most effective, and sometimes only, way that the encephalopathic diseases can be transmitted from one animal to another is by injection. Some species seem, however, to be remarkably resistant, or even completely immune, to the transmissible agent. Man clearly can acquire some forms of spongiform encephalopathy, e.g. Kuru, from within the species but as far as we know it cannot be transmitted to man from any other species.

Just as human beings do not seem to be susceptible to the virus that causes foot and mouth disease in many farm animals, they seem not to be susceptible to the causative agent of BSE, whatever it may be. This does not mean that transmission could not possibly occur under experimental conditions, as the production of spongiform encephalopathy in a pig by the injection of massive amounts of brain extract from infected cows has recently indicated. Certainly in a world in which risks are inevitable, merely as a consequence of living, the risk of acquiring BSE from eating meat from healthy cows would seem to be so small as to be insignificant. That is, of course, a matter of opinion.

Since the facts upon which to base a numerical judgment are just not available—nor I suspect ever likely to become so—it would appear prudent not to include cow brains or spinal cord in foods for human or animal consumption, since prions, whatever they may be, do seem to accumulate in neural tissue. The disadvantages of not using these tissues as food are very few and the advantages of using them even fewer; consequently the risks of using them, though probably extremely low, are not worth taking. This is not true for the other edible parts of apparently normal animals, where the benefits of eating them are high and the risks low.

5

Causes for Concern and a Possible Remedy

I hope that I have been able to show, by citing a few recent examples, that whilst much of the media coverage of food safety in healthy eating is hyped beyond belief—often to the point of absurdity—we should not ignore the genuine causes for concern that many of the stories contain. What is lacking in almost all of the stories is the sense of perspective that only wisdom or, more properly, knowledge tempered by mature judgment, can bring.

Questions of legitimate interest, and possible concern, such as the cause, nature, mode of spread and possible implications for human health and disease of BSE, for example, would have been investigated before the modern era of mass communication, by the scientific community, and the risk assessed before the debate reached the public arena. The information would have become available in something approaching a quantitative form such as already exists for many other diseases, and the panic reactions which we have seen and were largely due to ignorance—might have been avoided. The availability of information does not necessarily prevent hysterical responses, but the public reaction to BSE, Salmonella and the other recent food scares was undoubtedly fuelled by the inability of responsible scientists to answer many of the questions raised by honest sceptics as well as by opportunist speculators.

In my opinion only by increasing our investment in scientific research into human nutrition and on communicating the findings to the public through education are we ever going to protect ourselves from media hype such as that described in this paper. Education about the use and limitations of science and the scientific method must continue throughout school life if we are ever to have a population capable of distinguishing true from false prophets. That this does not happen at the present time is self-evident and is, I believe, because an understanding of science and the scientific method is still not considered to be an essential part of a proper education.

Recent events, which are not confined to food safety and nutritional issues, illustrate how false such a view is. The move against science and technology which I have called Technophobia is one of the most important causes for concern for the future of our society, which depends for its continued health and prosperity so heavily upon science and technology.

Irrational outbursts and hysterical headlines in newspapers and on television about the rainforests, ozone layer, carbon dioxide accumulation, nuclear power and so on, which are supported by repetitive exposure isolated and unrepresentative incidents intended to arouse emotions rather than impart information, are no substitute for informed debate. They are, however, the infected meat of politics, against which there is no antidote except education and knowledge based upon facts and not upon prejudice and rhetoric.

Government has an important responsibility to re-establish public confidence in science to which we owe our present opportunity to live longer and in better health than ever before despite anything that its detractors may say or imply to the contrary.

NOTES

1 Efron E., *The Apocalyptics: How Environmental Politics Controls What We Know About Cancer*, Simon and Schuster, New York: 1984.

2 Digby Anderson, *The Times*, Tuesday 12 March, 1985.

3 Barsky, J., 'The Paradox of Health', *New England Journal of Medicine*, 318, 1988, pp. 414-418.

4 Zacher, H., Head of Max Plank Society: Munich, cited *Scientific European*, October, 1990, p. 8.

5 Paracelsus, a famous 16th Century German chemist and philosopher who is generally looked upon as the father of modern scientific toxicology.

6 Sir Donald Acheson, Chief Medical Officer, Department of Health, circular letter entitled 'Germanium-containing Dietary Supplements', 10th October,1989; Sir Donald Acheson, Chief Medical Officer, Department of Health, circular letter entitled 'L-Tryptophan and Eosinophilia Myalgia Syndrome', 6th September 1990.

7 Broad, W. and Wade, N., *Betrayers of the Truth*, Oxford: Oxford University Press, 1982; Altman, L. and Melcher, L., 'Fraud in Science', *British Medical Journal*, vol. 286, 1983, pp. 2003-2006; Angell, M. and Relman A.S., 'Fraud in Biomedical Research: A Time For Congressional Restraint', *New England Journal of Medicine,* vol, 38, 1988, pp. 1462-1463.

8 Marks, V., 'Exploding the myths about Sugar', in Anderson, D. (ed), *A Diet of Reason*, London: Social Affairs Unit, 1986, pp. 77-88.

9 Donovan, K.L. and Peters, J., 'Vegetableburger Allergy: all was nut as it appeared', *British Medical Journal*, vol. 300, 1990, p. 1378.

10 Gevitz, N., *Other Healers: Unorthodox Medicine in America*, Baltimore: John Hopkins Press, 1988.

11 Miller, D.R. and Hayes, K.C., 'Vitamin Excess and Toxicity', In Hathcock, J.N., (ed.), *Nutritional Toxicology*, New York: Academic Press, 1982; Hall, C., 'Warning Against Extra Vitamins', *The Independent*, 2nd October 1990.

12 Clifford, M.J. and Willson, K.C., (eds), *Coffee: Botany, Biochemistry and Production of Beans and Beverage*, London: Croom Helm, 1985; Clifford, M.J. and Willson, K.C., (eds), *Tea: Cultivation to Consumption*, Chapman & Hall, in press (due mid 1991).

13 Glinsmann, W.H., Irausquin, H. and Park, Y.K., Report from the FDA's Sugar Task Force, 1986, 'Evaluation of Health Aspects of Sugars contained in Carbohydrate Sweeteners', *Journal of Nutrition,* 1986, p. 116, S1-S216; COMA, Dietary Sugars and Human Disease, Department of Health Report on Health and Social Subjects, 37, HMSO, 1989.

14 See note above.

15 Reed, B., *Back to Basics 'How one probation officer uses nutrition to improve the health and maintain the attention of clients referred by the Court'*, Privately printed and distributed, 1977.

16 Brynjolfsson, A., 'Wholesomeness of irradiated foods: a review', *Journal of Food Safety*, vol. 7, 1985, pp. 107-126.

17 Roberts, D., 'Sources of infection: Food', *The Lancet*, 335, 1990, pp. 859-861.

18 Praisiner, S.B., 'Prions and Neurodegenerative Disease', *New England Journal of Medicine*, vol. 317, 1987, pp. 1571-1581.